SUMMER
ACTIVITY BOOK

Clare Beaton

BARRON'S

- Always be very great careful with sharp tools, such as scissors, needles, and knives. Ask a grown-up for help.
- Always cover work surfaces with newspaper before you start to paint or varnish your work.
- When using a craft knife, always cut away from hands. Use thick cardboard under whatever you are cutting. Cut slowly and lightly several times.

This symbol is to remind you to be careful.

Adult supervision is recommended when children are using a craft knife.

Some basic tools and materials:
paint and brushes
varnish
glue
scissors and craft knife
paper and cardboard
colored pencils and felt-tip pens

This butterfly will be fluttering through the pages with you. See if you can spot it each time.

Matchbox chest

Make this chest to keep a collection of small things: beads, seeds, pins, and so on.

What you will need
★ 6 matchboxes
★ glue and clear tape
★ plain or patterned paper
★ 6 beads
★ thin wire

1

Stick the matchboxes together using the glue.

2

Cover the top, back, and sides with the paper of your choice.

3 Push 2 in. (5 cm) wire through bead and front of "drawer."

Twist ends together and secure with clear tape.

Make handles with beads and wire for the fronts of matchboxes.

Look for pretty stones, shells, feathers, and seeds when you are out for a walk or on the beach.

They can all be used for making the vacation picture on page 13. You could also use the shells you find to make the shell box on page 22.

The things you have collected will also look nice displayed in jars and boxes.

Stick boxes together on their sides to make a large "display case" with lots of compartments.

Fill a glass jar or bottle with attractive, clean stones and cover with water. Top off water as it slowly evaporates.

You can paint the boxes all one color or different colors then let dry before sticking on your bits and pieces.

Old buttons look good arranged together.

Pleated paper fans

What you will need
★ paper (see below)
★ cardboard
★ clear tape
★ scissors
★ paint, brushes, and glitter
  (if you want)

Decorating your fans
Here are some ideas:
• Use colored paper or patterned paper, like wallpaper samples or old wrapping paper.
• Cut a lacy pattern in plain white paper (see opposite).
  • Lay the finished fan on newspaper and flick paint on it with a brush.
  • Paint thick lines along the shape of the open fan using different colors.
  • Sprinkle glitter on the wet paint.

1
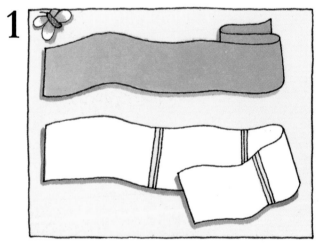
Make a strip of paper 60 in. (152 cm) long and 7 in. (18 cm) wide by joining pieces of paper together.

2

Start at one end and fold the paper into ¾ in. (2 cm) wide pleats.

3 Just cut a few pleats at a time.

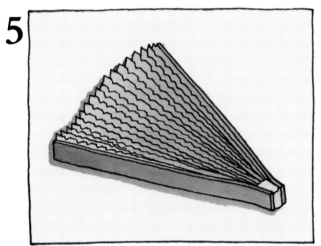

For a lacy fan cut out small pieces along one or both sides of the pleats.

4

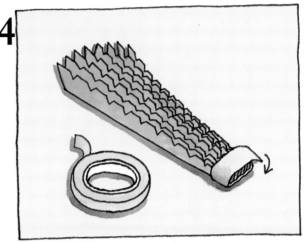

Bind one end of the folded fan firmly with clear tape.

5

Cut out two cardboard strips $3/4 \times$ 7 in. (2×18 cm). Stick along outer edges of fan. Open the fan out.

For a circular fan cut two cardboard strips $3/4 \times 12$ in. (2 cm $\times 30$ cm). Stick along outer edges of fan, but not covering tape.   Open fan.

Lemonade

What you will need

To make 1 qt. (1.2 L)
- ★ pitcher
- ★ 4 lemons
- ★ 1 qt. (1.2 L) water
- ★ 1/3 cup (75 g) superfine sugar
- ★ lemon squeezer and sharp knife
- ★ saucepan and wooden spoon

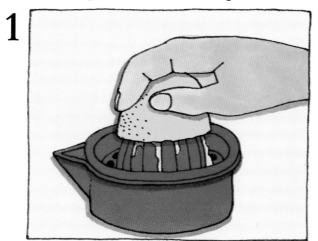

1 Ask a grown-up to help you cut the lemons in half. Squeeze. Pour the juice into the pitcher.

Rub lemon around a glass edge and dip in sugar.

2 Ask a grown-up to help you melt the sugar in the water. Stir over low heat until dissolved.

3 Add this syrup to the lemon juice. Stir and cool in refrigerator. Serve with ice.

Ice pops

What you will need
- ★ diluted fruit juice
- ★ fruit pieces (if you want)
- ★ molds or yogurt containers
- ★ ice cream sticks
- ★ tinfoil
- ★ tray or freezer-proof dish

You can also make "mini" pops in an ice tray with toothpicks. Cut the sharp points off the toothpicks before using them.

1 Twist center of strip around stick and bend ends over edges of molds.

Hold the stick in place and keep upright in mold using a twisted strip of tinfoil. Place on the tray.

2

If you want to put in pieces of fruit, such as orange, strawberry, melon, or grape, do so now, carefully.

3

Pour in the fruit juice up to the edge. Place the tray carefully in the freezer. Leave until frozen.

Visor

What you will need
★ thin cardboard
★ tracing paper
★ soft pencil
★ craft knife and scissors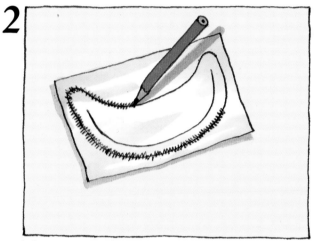
★ clear tape
★ paint and brushes or pens and decorations of your choice

1

Trace the pattern on the opposite page (including the dotted line), using tracing paper and pencil.

2

Turn over the tracing paper and scribble over lines with the soft pencil.

3

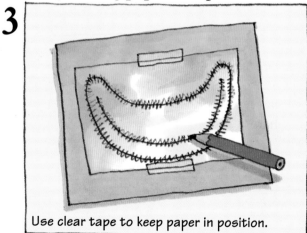

Use clear tape to keep paper in position.

Turn over and retrace along lines onto thin cardboard. Cut out inside line with knife and outside with scissors.

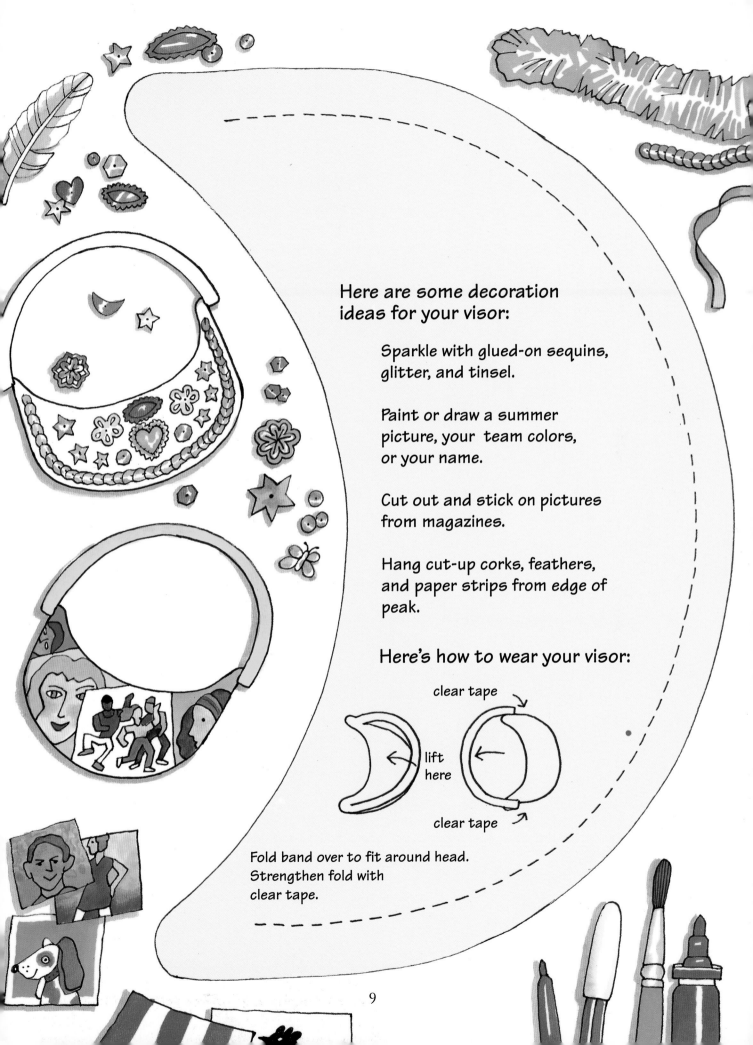

Here are some decoration
ideas for your visor:

Sparkle with glued-on sequins,
glitter, and tinsel.

Paint or draw a summer
picture, your team colors,
or your name.

Cut out and stick on pictures
from magazines.

Hang cut-up corks, feathers,
and paper strips from edge of
peak.

Here's how to wear your visor:

clear tape

lift
here

clear tape

Fold band over to fit around head.
Strengthen fold with
clear tape.

Summer jewelry

Here are some ideas for making wonderful, funky summer jewelry for yourself, or as gifts for your family and friends. Have lots of fun collecting:

seeds   pasta shapes

corks   shells and stones (with holes)

Before you begin
- Cover your work surface.
- Be careful when you use a craft knife or needle.
- Check the length of the necklace or bracelet.

You could start with this simple necklace.

string or strip of leather

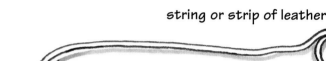

stone or shell with hole

Melon seed necklace

What you will need
★ melon
★ thread
★ strainer and paper towels
★ sharp needle
★ paint and brush (if you want)

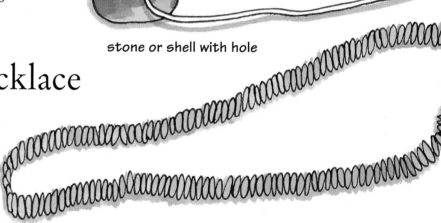

1
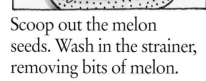
Scoop out the melon seeds. Wash in the strainer, removing bits of melon.

2

Lay the seeds out on paper towels to dry thoroughly.

3 Paint seeds if you like.

Using the sharp needle, thread seeds onto thread. Tie ends together.

Cork bracelet

What you will need
★ corks and beads
★ paint, varnish, and brushes
★ large needle and thin elastic
★ craft knife

1

Ask a grown-up to help cut each cork into four pieces.

2

Paint the corks in bright colors and leave to dry. Varnish.

3

Thread onto elastic with needle, alternating with beads. Tie ends together.

Pasta pin

What you will need
★ thick cardboard and scissors
★ pasta shapes
★ glue, paint, brushes, varnish
★ safety pin and clear tape

1

This could be any shape you like.

Cut out the cardboard shape.

2

Arrange and glue on the pasta shapes you have selected.

3

Paint if you like.

When dry turn it over and tape on the safety pin. Varnish.

Souvenir scrap book

Make a simple scrap book with souvenirs of your vacation. Whether you go away or stay at home, collect lots of "scraps," such as photos, stamps, coins, wrappers, and tickets.

What you will need

★ 1 sheet of thin cardboard
★ sheets of plain paper for pages
★ needle and yarn or ribbon
★ scissors and glue

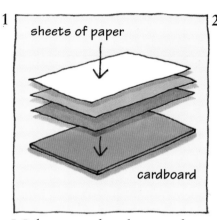

1

sheets of paper

cardboard

Make sure the sheets of paper and cardboard are the same size. Place paper on top of cardboard. Fold everything in half.

2

Open and sew together along middle crease with needle and yarn.

3

Tie the two ends together tightly in a bow.

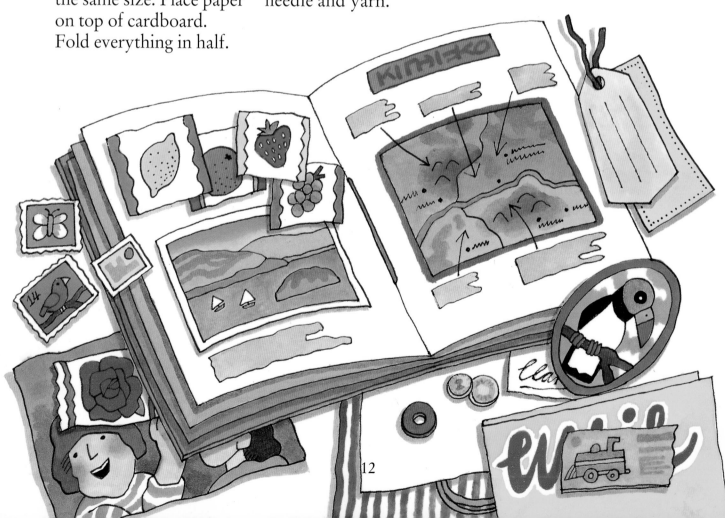

Windmills

What you will need to make two windmills
- ★ 2 2½ in. (6 cm) lengths of thin wire
  (gardening wire or opened paper clips)
- ★ 4 beads
- ★ 2 thin sticks (firm straws will do)
- ★ clear tape
- ★ scissors

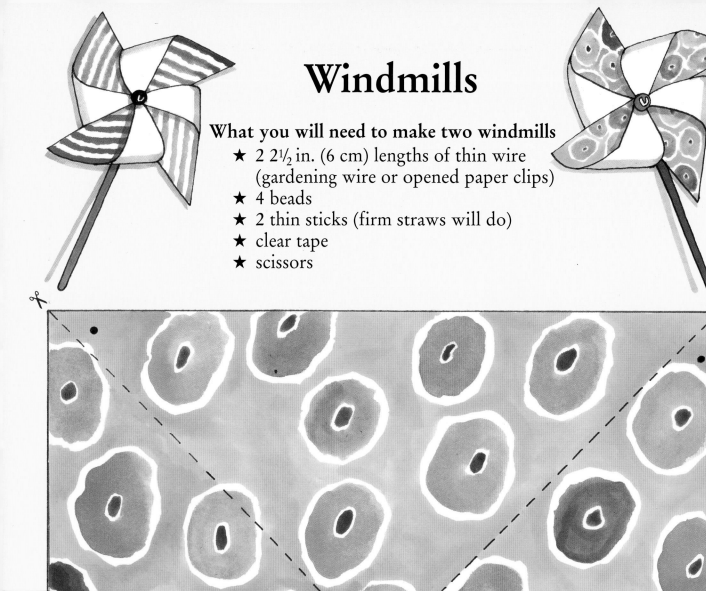

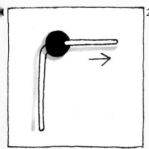

Bend the wire to 90° in center. Thread a bead down to the corner.

Press out windmills. Carefully cut along the dotted lines.

Push wire through center from the back, then pick up and push on each dotted corner in turn (clockwise).

Hold with fingers. Thread on second bead. Bend the end of the wire to hold in place.

Tape wire firmly to stick at back. Flatten sails slightly so they revolve easily. Wave to spin.

Vacation collage

Make a special collage of your best souvenirs from your vacation or outing. Here's how you can frame them. They'll remind you of summer all through the year!

What you will need
★ corrugated cardboard
★ craft knife
★ glue
★ pencil and ruler

1

Cut two pieces of cardboard the same size.

2

Cut out a hole inside one piece of cardboard to make a frame.

3

Glue the frame piece on top of other piece of cardboard. Decorate frame.

Collect autographs of people you meet. Take their photographs.

Decorate the frame with paint, or glue pictures onto it – you could cover it with maps.

Potpourri

You can vary the flowers and herbs you use to achieve different smells. Try a mixture of lavender and honeysuckle. Concentrated flower oils are available from specialty stores.

What you will need
★ scented rose petals
★ scented flowers and herbs
★ 1 orange and 1 lemon
★ 1 tablespoon mixed spice
★ concentrated lavender or rose oil
★ paper towels and baking sheet
★ jar with screw cover
★ grater and large bowl

1

Pull off petals and dry on paper towels away from sunlight. Turn over twice a day until completely dry.

2

Grate the lemon and orange peel onto a baking sheet and ask a grown-up to put it into a warm oven to dry.

3

Put the dried peel in the large bowl and add petals, mixed spice, and a few drops of flower oil. Mix well.

4

Store in the jar with the cover on. Put into a pretty bowl to make your room smell nice.

Rosewater

You can use this in the bath, and to cool your face and hands.

What you will need
★ 2 handfuls of scented rose petals
★ 1 cup (225 g) sugar
★ 1 qt. (1.2 L) water
★ large bowl
★ saucepan and wooden spoon
★ strainer and clean jars with covers

1

Pull the petals carefully off the stems and put into a large bowl.

2

With the help of a grown-up, slowly dissolve the sugar in the water, stirring over a low heat.

3

Pour over the rose petals and leave for 1 hour. Stir thoroughly and leave for another hour.

4

You could make pretty labels and stick them on the jars.

Strain and pour into the jars. The rosewater will last for about a week, kept in the refrigerator.

Fun on the beach

Can you spot ten differences between these two pictures?

Painting stones

When you are out, walking or playing, collect interesting shaped stones. Choose big, smooth ones that you can paint pictures on like the ones shown below.

What you will need
★ large smooth stones
★ thick paint and brushes
★ varnish
★ pencil

Wash the stones and leave them to dry. Decide what you are going to paint on your stone and start by painting the base color all over. Draw out details with pencil when dry, and then paint, leaving each color to dry before adding the next. Varnish.

Super jet

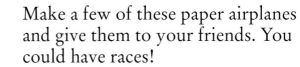

Make a few of these paper airplanes and give them to your friends. You could have races!

Follow the dotted lines as carefully as you can when folding.

1

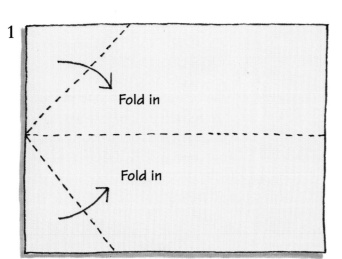

Fold in

Fold in

Fold paper in half lengthwise. Open and fold corners down at one end.

What you will need

★ plain or colored paper, cut to $8^{1}/_{4} \times 11^{5}/_{8}$ in. (210 × 296 mm)
★ felt-tip pens or colored pencils and decorations of your choice
★ scissors

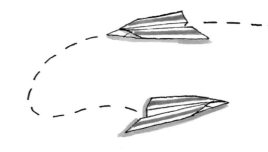

2

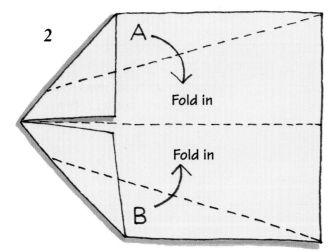

A

Fold in

Fold in

B

Fold down sides, making sure points A and B meet in middle.

3

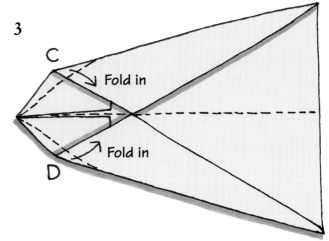

C

Fold in

Fold in

D

Fold in points C and D, making sure these meet in middle. Turn the plane over carefully.

4

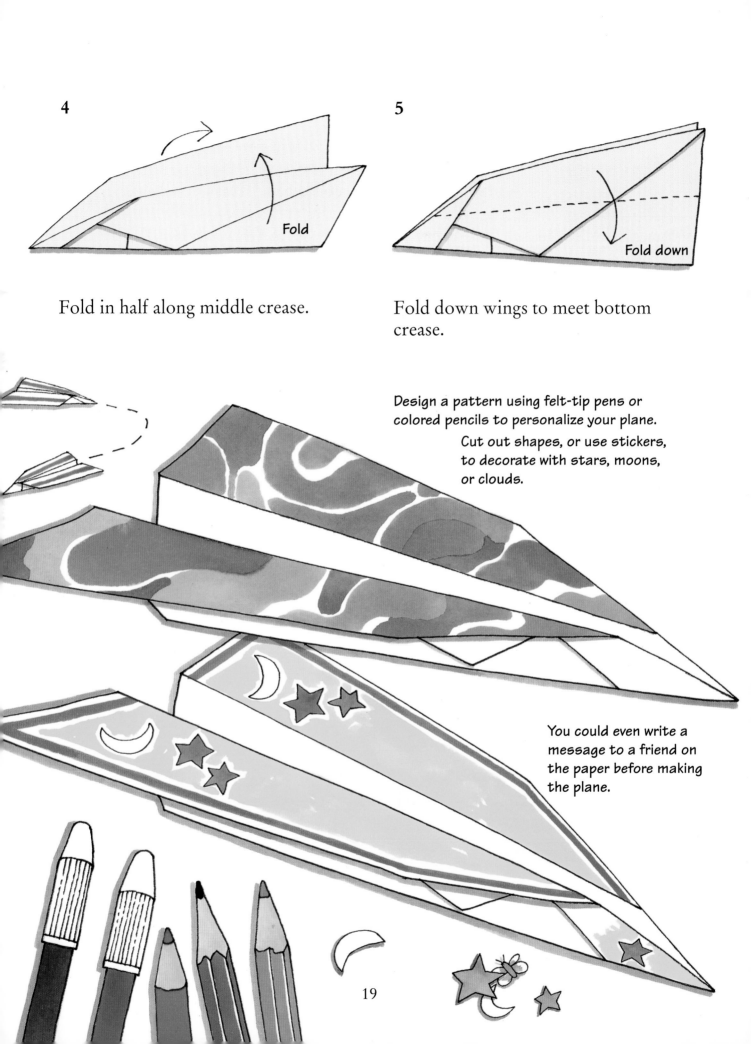

Fold in half along middle crease.

5

Fold down wings to meet bottom crease.

Design a pattern using felt-tip pens or colored pencils to personalize your plane.

Cut out shapes, or use stickers, to decorate with stars, moons, or clouds.

You could even write a message to a friend on the paper before making the plane.

It's great fun decorating ice cream with delicious sweets and sauces.

What you will need
★ wafers and cones
★ fruit and nuts
★ cake decorations
★ candies and ladyfingers

Butterscotch sauce
2 tablespoons (50 g) butter
4 level tablespoons brown sugar
2 level tablespoons corn syrup
Ask a grown-up to help you melt all the ingredients in a saucepan over low heat. Boil for 1 minute.

Chocolate sauce
$\frac{1}{3}$ cup (75 g) superfine sugar
$\frac{1}{3}$ cup (75 g) brown sugar
$\frac{1}{3}$ cup (75 g) cocoa powder
$1\frac{1}{4}$ cups (300 ml) milk
1 teaspoon vanilla extract
1 tablespoon (25 g) butter

Ask a grown-up to help you and put all ingredients in a saucepan over low heat. Stir until sugar has dissolved. Slowly bring to a boil. Boil without stirring for 5 minutes.

Parfait
Put layers of ice cream, fruit, and sauce into a tall glass and decorate top.

Ice cream boat
Cut a wafer into two triangles and stick into a scoop of ice cream in a sauce sea.

Cone faces
Make faces with candies – pour a little sauce on top and sprinkle with nuts or cake decorations. Make ears out of ladyfingers.

Matching pairs

Can you find the matching pair in each row?

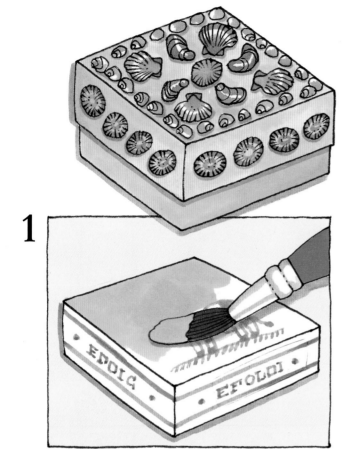

What you will need
★ shells
★ box with top
★ varnish
★ glue and glue brush
★ thick paint and brush

Before you begin
- Plan your shells, making sure you have enough to cover the box top and create your own design.
- You can make a regular or random design as shown below.

1

Paint the box all over, covering any lettering or pictures. Leave to dry.

2
Start in the middle of the box.

Put a dab of glue on each shell and press firmly into position onto the top of the box.

3
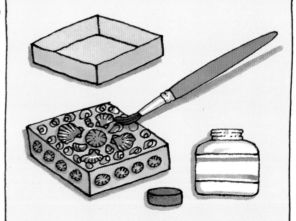

Stick shells around the edge of the box if you want. When dry, brush shells with varnish.

- Create your own sculptures in a sandbox or on the beach. Make a monster, funny faces, or a car, boat, or rocket.
- Get your friends to help and make something really big!
- Using damp sand, make different shapes with clean yogurt containers. Form large shapes with your hands, patting down the sand firmly.

- Make patterns with a stick or by pressing down the edges or bottoms of containers.
- Decorate with anything you can find. Seaweed and leaves make wonderful hair. Make faces or interesting patterns with feathers, stones, shells, and sticks.

Use a paper plate for a steering wheel.

Finish off your monster/dinosaur with a row of small sand castles, with pointed shells and grass, along its back.

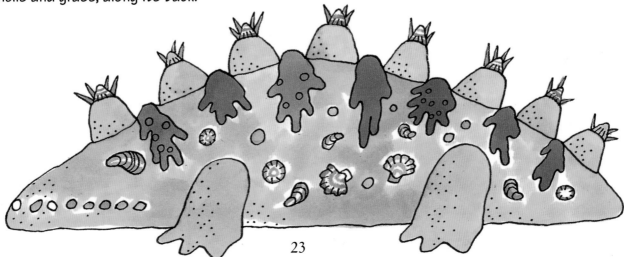

Here are two simple games you can play with pebbles or stones. Wash the stones if necessary.

Stone circle
(for two players)

You could play this game indoors or out.

- Put 15 stones in a circle and decide who starts.
- The first player picks up a number of stones – either one, two, or three.
- The other player does the same.
- Take turns until there are no stones left.
- The winner is the player who has an odd number of stones.

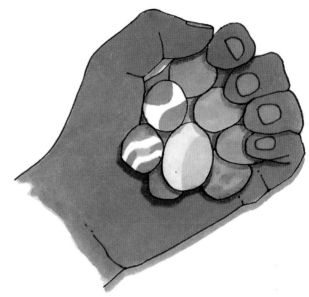

Hands full

Play this with any number of friends – but make sure you all have about the same size hands!

The aim of this game is to see who can hold the most stones in one hand. You could play it indoors or out.

- Collect a pile of stones or pebbles.
- Take turns to pick them up, one by one, with one hand and hold them in the other.
- Use the same pile of stones for each player.

First edition for the United States,
Canada, and the Philippines published 1994 by Barron's Educational Series, Inc.

Text and Illustrations © b small publishing 1994

All inquiries shoud be addressed to:
Barron's Educational Series, Inc.
250 Wireless Boulevard
Hauppauge, NY 11788

International Standard Book No. 0-8120-1959-8

Printed in Hong Kong

567   9598   98765432